LINE UP

The number line below is all jumbled. You need to move the numbers and their accompanying letters so the numbers are in order. When you've got them all in a line, put the letters in the blanks to find the answer to the riddle.

Which animal can balance a ball, swim, and lie perfectly flat?

0	-3	2	-1	7	4	1	-4
A	S	I	E	E	N	L	A

_ _ _ _ _ _ - _

Hint on page 46

Illustration: Bill Colrus

RECORD RESULTS

Carrie kept score for the Special Olympics. She marked down a lot of different results, but now it's

Softball Throw — Distance

Fekisha:
from the 1-foot line to the 11-foot line _____

Tawanna:
from the 2-foot line to the 18-foot line _____

Raul:
from the 6-foot line to the 20-foot line _____

Michael:
from the 4-foot line to the 12-foot line _____

5K Cycle Race — Time

Barclay: started at 1:11;
        finished at 1:19 _____

Carlos: started at 1:20;
        finished at 1:31 _____

Megan: started at 1:32;
        finished at 1:42 _____

Ian: started at 1:43;
        finished at 1:52 _____

Basketball Shots for Accuracy — Baskets

Alexis: 50 shots, 6 misses _____

Farouk: 49 shots, 3 misses _____

Ying: 49 shots, 4 misses _____

Ariana: 51 shots, 8 misses _____

Hint on page 46

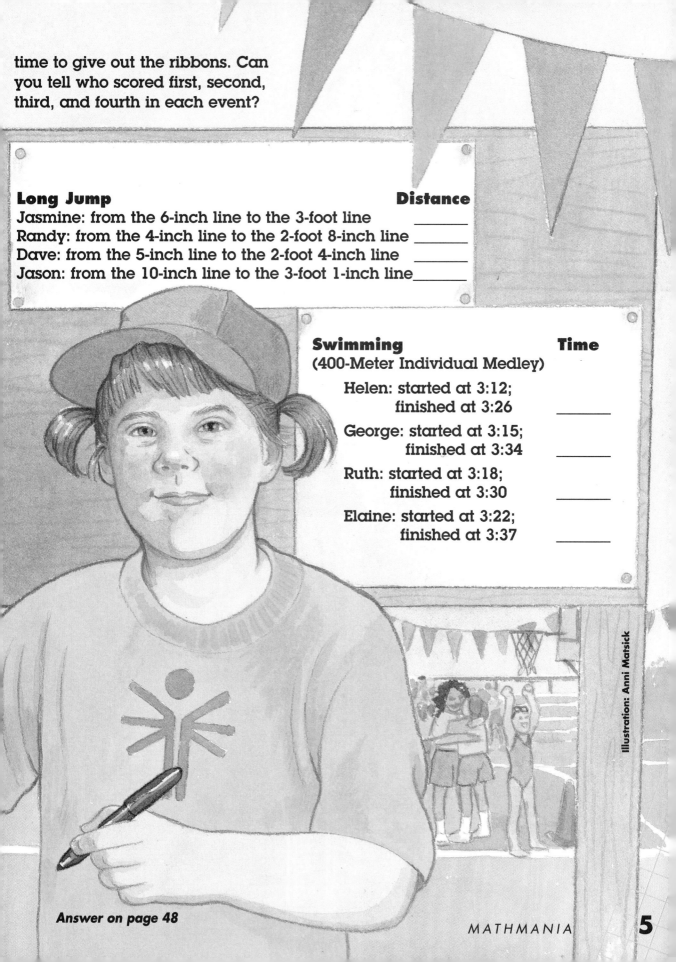

time to give out the ribbons. Can you tell who scored first, second, third, and fourth in each event?

Long Jump   **Distance**

Jasmine: from the 6-inch line to the 3-foot line _____

Randy: from the 4-inch line to the 2-foot 8-inch line _____

Dave: from the 5-inch line to the 2-foot 4-inch line _____

Jason: from the 10-inch line to the 3-foot 1-inch line _____

Swimming   **Time**
(400-Meter Individual Medley)

Helen: started at 3:12;
        finished at 3:26   _____

George: started at 3:15;
        finished at 3:34   _____

Ruth: started at 3:18;
        finished at 3:30   _____

Elaine: started at 3:22;
        finished at 3:37   _____

Illustration: Anni Matsick

Answer on page 48

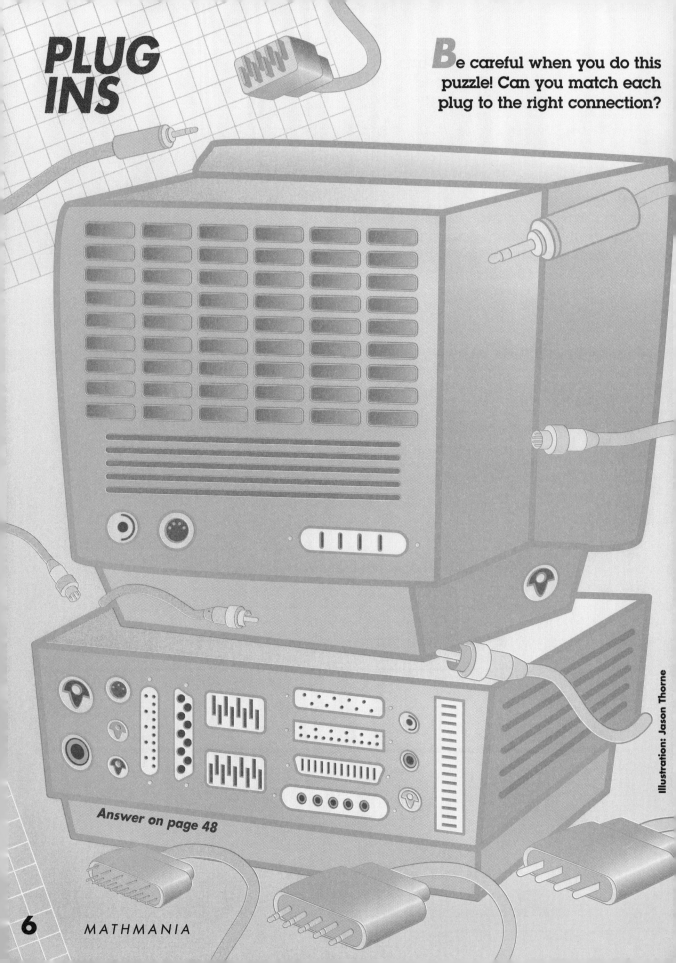

PLUG INS

Be careful when you do this puzzle! Can you match each plug to the right connection?

Answer on page 48

Illustration: Jason Thorne

TAKING TEMPERATURES

Gillian measured the temperature for a week. Can you answer her questions based on the information shown?

Hint on page 46

| | Temperature | |
	High	Low
Saturday	68°	63°
Sunday	67°	58°
Monday	59°	49°
Tuesday	63°	55°
Wednesday	70°	62°
Thursday	68°	62°
Friday	65°	57°

1. What was the warmest day of the week? _____
2. What was the coolest day of the week? _____
3. What was the average high temperature for the week? _____
4. What was the average low temperature for the week? _____

Answer on page 48

WEIGHTING ROOM

It's very busy in the Valley Vet clinic today. All these animals need to weigh in before the

COPPERHEAD

WEIGHTS

	OWNER	ANIMAL
Philip	84	
Daniel	97	Goldie
Chris	142	Copperhead
Joan	123	Ironside
Prudence	106	Tiny
Ruby	139	Silver
		Polo

doctor can see them. Can you help figure out each animal's weight?

Illustration: Rick Geary

POLO

IRONSIDE

GOLDIE

TINY

145

176

115

131

Hint on page 46

MATHMANIA **9**

STACKING STANLEY

Stan needs to unstack all these boxes. There are no holes or openings behind the boxes. How many boxes are in this stack?

Illustration: R. Michael Palan

Answer on page 48

DOTS A LOT

Count by 3s to connect these dots and reveal the start of something big.

204

201 • • 210 • 207

276

273 • • 279
282

198
195 • • 213
192 •

177

189
186 • • 180   219   225
183   216 •   222   • 228   267
• 174   264 • • 270
                    231   • 261
                255 258 • 246
                    • 249
            234   • 285
                252
            • 237   243
                240
• 171
                            • 3
• 168   102 •   • 6

165 • 108   • 105   36 •
111   96 •   • 9
                                33 •
                                        12
162 •   93 • • 42   45 • • 39   18 • • 15
        114   45 •   30 •   • 21
159 •   • 117   • 27 • 24
        • 120
        138

        90 •   • 48
    87 •   • 51
            • 69

156 •   141
        • 135 • 123
153 •   144 •
150 •   • 126
    147 132 • 129

        84 •
            72 • • 66
        • 81   • 63
        78 75   • 54
            60 • 51

Illustration: Rob Sepanak

PLAY THE DOZENS

These twelve clues should give you a lot of information about 12.

Spell out each answer in the correct boxes within the grid, one letter per box.

ACROSS

1. 12 of these pass from noon to midnight.
4. 12 of anything
5. 12 _____ 12 equals 144.
6. A baker's dozen
10. 1 trillion has 12 of these.
11. 6 of one plus a half-dozen of another equals this many.
12. 2 hexagons have 12 of these.

DOWN

2. XII is 12 in these type of numerals.
3. There are 12 of these in a year.
7. There are 12 of these in a foot.
8. 144 inches equals 12 of these.
9. There are 12 dozen in this measure.

Answer on page 49

Illustration: R. Michael Palan

UPS AND DOWNS

Floors

10
9
8
7
6
5
4
3
2
1

Illustration: Bill Colrus

- Ellie lives 3 floors above Darren and 1 floor below Jen.
- Tyler never needs the elevator or stairs to reach his apartment.
- Ben lives just above Craig.
- Darren lives 1 floor above Tyler and 5 floors below Stephanie.
- Myra has to ride the elevator all the way to the top to reach her floor.
- Craig lives on a floor between Darren and Ellie.
- Christina lives 1 floor above Jason.

Hint on page 46

14 *MATHMANIA* **Answer on page 49**

100 DUCKS

Can you pick three lucky ducks that equal 100?

Hint on page 46

Answer on page 49

Illustration: R. Michael Palan

KEEP MUM

M. Balmer, the National Museum's curator, is wrapping up for the day. Before these mummies could be sent to the museum, they needed to be rewrapped for protection.

Mimi
72 inches

Illustration: Michael Austin

Now he needs to figure out how much wrapping he used. If each roll of wrapping covers $1\frac{1}{2}$ feet of a person's height, how much wrapping did the curator use today?

Hint on page 46

Minnie 90 inches

Mamie 63 inches

Max 54 inches

Fred 81 inches

SIMONE SAYS

Simone is painting some new creations. Can you tell how many faces she has to paint on the sides of each set of blocks? She doesn't need to paint the sides that touch one another, but she does want to paint faces on the bottom of the sets.

Ⓐ Ⓑ Ⓒ Ⓓ Ⓔ Ⓕ

Illustration: R. Michael Palan

Answer on page 49

18

FIND 50

All the rows except one and all the columns except one have numbers that equal 50 when added together. Can you find the one row and one column?

10	6	4	2	10	10	8
6	4	10	10	9	1	10
1	10	6	4	10	9	10
10	8	10	10	10	7	3
4	10	9	6	1	10	10
10	2	10	8	3	10	7
9	10	1	10	7	3	10

Answer on page 49

GET COORDINATED

To find the answer to this riddle, fill in each blank with a letter from the grid. The numbers beneath each blank match a coordinate on the grid. The first number tells you how many lines to count across the

Why doesn't the piano work?

___ ___   ___ ___ ___ ___
4,3   7,6   5,5   1,11   11,3   2,9

___ ___ ___ ___ ___   ___ ___ ___
9,7   11,11   0,7   8,4   4,10   3,7   7,2   5,0

___ ___   ___ ___ ___ ___ .
10,9   6,8   2,5   1,2   8,10   3,1

Answer on page 49

bottom, while the second number tells you how many rows to count up. For example, the numbers under the first blank tell you that you want to go across 4 and then up 3 to the *I*.

ODDS OR EVENS

Try this puzzle without doing the actual math work. Estimate the answer, and then see if you can come up with any rules that will help.

The object is to figure out whether the answer to each problem will be an odd number or an even number.

1. 23 + 37

2. 15 + 42

3. 26 + 28

4. 13 × 17

5. 20 × 32

6. 19 × 24

7. 37 − 23

8. 42 − 15

9. 28 − 26

10. 221 ÷ 17

Answer on page 49

Illustration: John Nez

SCRAMBLED PICTURE

Copy these mixed-up wedges into the spaces on the next page to unscramble this picture.

A1

A6

B6

A3

B1

B2

B5

B3

A2

A4

B4

A5

The letters and numbers tell you where each wedge belongs. The first one, A3, has been done for you.

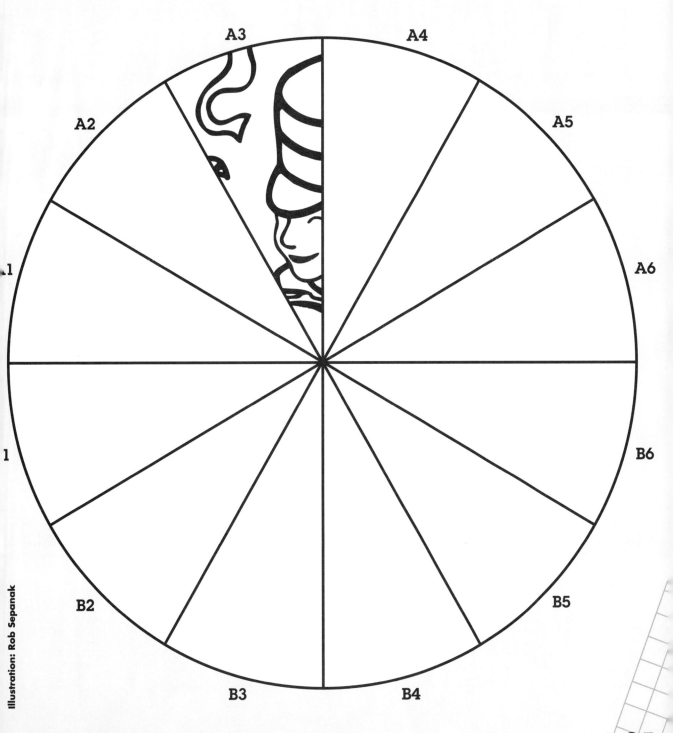

WHAT'S THE PATTERN?

Can you tell which of the two choices is the next design in each row?

A   **B**

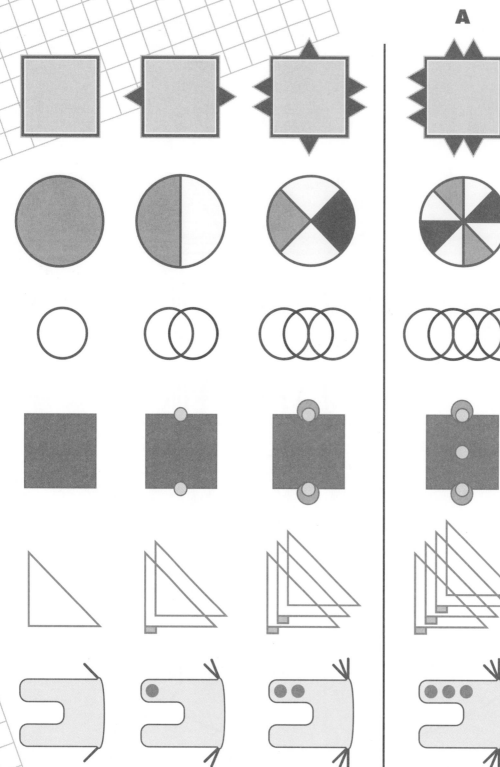
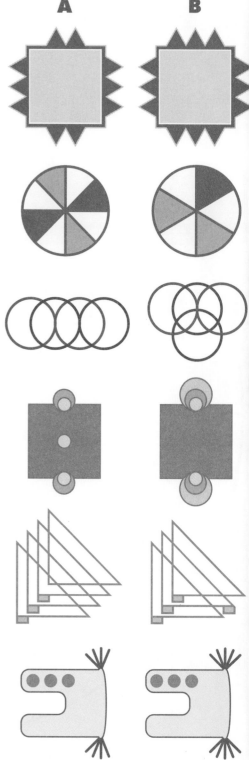

Answer on page 50

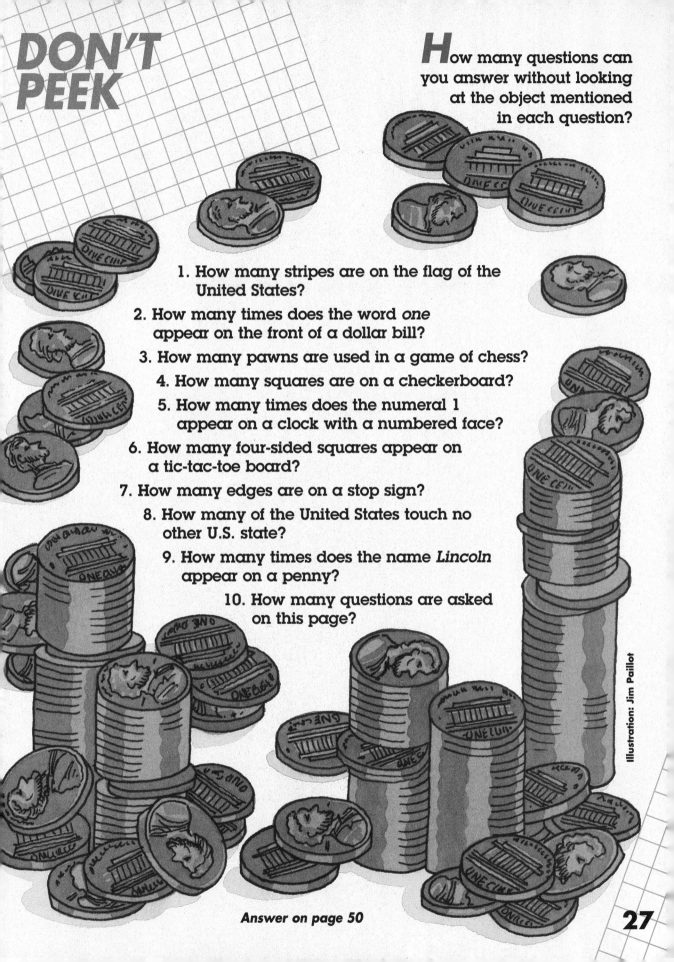

DON'T PEEK

How many questions can you answer without looking at the object mentioned in each question?

1. How many stripes are on the flag of the United States?

2. How many times does the word *one* appear on the front of a dollar bill?

3. How many pawns are used in a game of chess?

4. How many squares are on a checkerboard?

5. How many times does the numeral 1 appear on a clock with a numbered face?

6. How many four-sided squares appear on a tic-tac-toe board?

7. How many edges are on a stop sign?

8. How many of the United States touch no other U.S. state?

9. How many times does the name *Lincoln* appear on a penny?

10. How many questions are asked on this page?

Illustration: Jim Paillot

Answer on page 50

UPWARD BOUND

You'll scale new heights if you finish this puzzle. The heights of some of the world's most exotic mountains are hidden here. The heights can be found

MOUNTAIN	HEIGHT (in feet)	LOCATION
	20,873	Bolivia
Illampu	19,931	Peru
Chachani	19,340	Tanzania
Kilimanjaro	17,058	Kenya
Kenya	16,763	Uganda-Zaire
Margherita Peak	16,500	New Guinea
Jaja	15,771	France-Italy
Mount Blanc	15,585	New Guinea
Trikora	15,420	New Guinea
Mandala	15,158	Ethiopia
Ras Dashan	14,979	Tanzania
Meru	14,787	Zaire-Rwanda
Karisimbi	14,178	Kenya-Uganda
Elgon	14,154	Switzerland
Grand Combin	14,131	Ethiopia
Batu	13,881	Ethiopia
Guna	13,780	Ethiopia
Gughe	13,661	Morocco
Toubkal	13,455	Malaysia
Kinabalu	13,353	Cameroon
Cameroon	12,467	Sumatra
Kerinci	12,349	New Zealand
Cook	12,198	Canary Islands
Teide	12,060	Java
Semeru	7,310	Australia
Kosciusko	4,393	United States
Mansfield		

across, up, down, diagonally, or backward. Circle each number as you find it. Some numerals may appear in more than one answer, and every numeral will be used at least once.

Illustration: Bill Colrus

```
2 7 6 4 2 1 1 1 0
0 4 3 9 1 3 4 5 2
8 0 3 9 3 4 7 7 4
7 1 5 5 8 5 8 7 5
3 4 3 6 8 5 7 1 1
1 9 9 3 1 2 0 6 0
0 7 4 5 1 4 1 7 8
8 9 1 2 1 3 6 6 1
9 4 3 2 1 4 1 3 1
```

Answer on page 50

CAN CAN

Cal is trying to match the color of her paint from a catalog. She knows a few things about the code number she's looking for. Review the facts below and see if you can tell which can she wants.

Hint on page 47

Answer on page 50

Illustration: Diana Zourelias

27140

16895

39742

75835

41760

89318

50830

91780

62935

62385

The number of the can
- is evenly divisible by 5
- has 3 odd digits
- has a digit in the hundreds place that is larger than the digit in the tens place

CIRCLE SURPRISE

Divide this circle into six sections by using only three straight lines. The trick is that three numbers must appear in each section, and they must add up to 18.

Illustration: Marc Nadel

Answer on page 50

Hint on page 47

SUPER SHOPPER

Tyler's helping his mom shop for groceries. All the products they need to buy are on the table. Can you help him decide which coupon offers the best buy on each item?

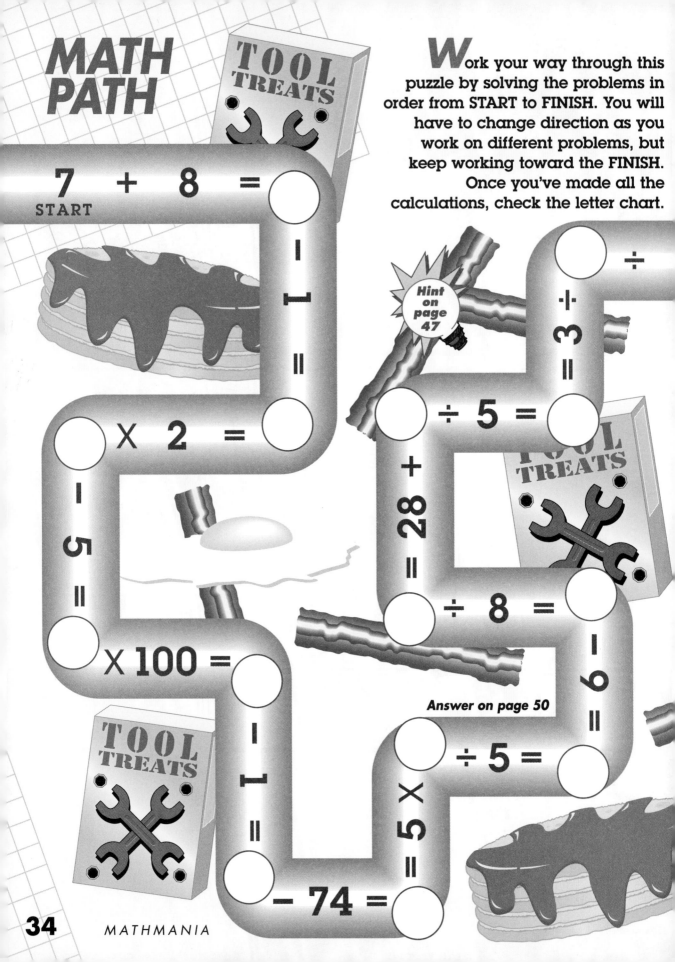

MATH PATH

TOOL TREATS

Work your way through this puzzle by solving the problems in order from START to FINISH. You will have to change direction as you work on different problems, but keep working toward the FINISH. Once you've made all the calculations, check the letter chart.

7 + 8 =
START

− 1 =

× 2 =

− 5 =

× 100 =

= 28 +

÷ 5 =

= 3 ÷

÷

÷ 5 =

÷ 8 =

= 6 −

÷ 5 =

Hint on page 47

TOOL TREATS

TOOL TREATS

Answer on page 50

− 1 =

5 × =

− 74 =

Put the letters in the blanks in the order you found the answers on the path. For example: 7 + 8 = 15. So 15 is the first number found. The chart says 15 matches the letter *P*. So a *P* goes on the first blank in the riddle. If you work back and forth, you should solve this riddle in no time.

$- 71 =$

FINISH

$- 1 =$

$\div 7 =$

$\times 7 =$

$=$

$- 12 =$

$\times 10$

$\div 10 =$

What do _ _ _ _ _ _ _ _ _ _ eat

for _ _ _ _ _ _ _ _ _ _ ?

_ _ _ _ _ _ _ _ _ _ _ _

$\times 10 =$

0-!	30-T
2-M	36-F
3-W	42-S
5-B	48-N
6-A	50-T
7-U	56-H
8-C	60-A
10-A	70-S
11-R	71-T
12-K	88-E
14-L	100-O
15-P	125-R
21-R	199-E
24-E	200-B
25-S	

$\div 7 =$

$+ 3 =$

$\times 2 =$

$\times 2 =$

$\div 6 =$

$+ 6 =$

$\times 7 =$

Illustration: Jason Thorne

DECIMAL DILEMMA

Hint on page 47

Can you match each fraction to its closest decimal value?

Illustration: David Helton

Answer on page 50

1/2

1/4

1/3

3/4

2/3

.67

.75

.50

.33

.25

CROSS OUTS

We've just uncovered Wilbert the Clown's greatest joke. To find it, follow the clues to cross out some of the boxes. Then write the remaining letters in the blanks, going from left to right and top to bottom.

Cross out the numbers in which
- one of the digits is an 8
- both digits are odd
- the sum of the digits is 10
- the difference between the two digits is 5
- the sum of the digits is less than 8

35 D	41 Y	85 G	62 A	32 I	94 S	71 X	27 J	45 C
14 A	76 O	57 W	72 H	67 W	20 B	91 F	46 R	61 S
52 K	31 P	90 W	64 I	42 G	84 T	50 R	36 A	13 E
38 P	89 E	11 J	66 L	55 T	37 C	69 K	13 R	40 L
26 I	70 Q	59 T	77 D	21 O	96 N	16 T	75 A	81 C
25 Q	54 G	17 K	86 D	65 B	51 I	39 U	92 A	28 M
67 C	22 E	83 U	48 B	44 K	95 Z	12 E	43 L	29 W
49 H	60 T	80 V	36 A	18 A	34 M	74 R	80 N	19 B
15 O	47 D	58 L	33 M	97 F	71 S	24 N	68 I	99 R

Answer on page 50

Hint on page 47

Illustration: Marc Nadel

What has four legs and says, "Oom, oom?"

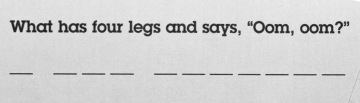

— ———— —————————

————————

TAPE TIMES

Veronica is in charge of making tapes for her dad's amateur film-maker customers. He left a list of videos and the running time of each.

Hint on page 47

Video 1
3 hours
Down in the Meadow
Needs to be completed at 5:30

Needs to be completed at 4:00
THE MILD BUNCH

Video 2
2½ hours

Now Veronica has to figure out when to start each tape in order to finish in time. Can you help her match each tape with the clock that has the right starting time?

The Itsy Bitsy Arachnid's Inclement Weather Difficulties
Needs to be completed at 4:45

Video 3
2 hours

Needs to be completed at 3:45
The Pizza Principle

Video 6
1½ hours

Needs to be completed at 3:30
Goofus and Gallant: The Movie

Video 4
1½ hours

Yet Another Sequel
Needs to be completed at 2:30

Arnie   Needs to be completed at 3:15

Video 7
3 hours

Needs to be completed at 3:00
The Purple Panther

Video 5
3 hours

Video 8
2½ hours

Answer on page 51

Illustration: Jerry Zimmerman

LIBRARY LAUGHS

Dewey has some funny books in his library. To check one out, solve each problem. Then go to the shelves to find the volume with the number that matches each answer. Put the matching letter in the blank beside each answer. Read down the letters you've filled in to find the title and author of the book Dewey just finished reading.

Illustration: Scott Peck

$16 \div 2 =$ ___ ___

$7 + 8 =$ ___ ___

$29 - 6 =$ ___ ___

$3 \times 3 =$ ___ ___

$24 \div 4 =$ ___ ___

$21 - 6 =$ ___ ___

$7 \times 3 =$ ___ ___

$9 + 5 =$ ___ ___

$12 \div 3 =$ ___ ___

$18 - 3 =$ ___ ___

$27 \div 3 =$ ___ ___

$6 \times 2 =$ ___ ___

$8 - 6 =$ ___ ___

$5 \times 5 =$ ___ ___

$3 + 1 =$ ___ ___

$25 - 10 =$ ___ ___

$23 - 2 =$ ___ ___

$21 \div 3 =$ ___ ___

$4 \times 1 =$ ___ ___

$10 - 5 =$ ___ ___

$10 \div 2 =$ ___ ___

$4 \times 4 =$ ___ ___

Answer on page 51

Hint on page 47

COLOR BY NUMBERS

Use the key to color the shapes.

1 dot—Tan	4 dots—Blue
2 dots—Yellow	5 dots—Gray
3 dots—Red	6 dots—Green

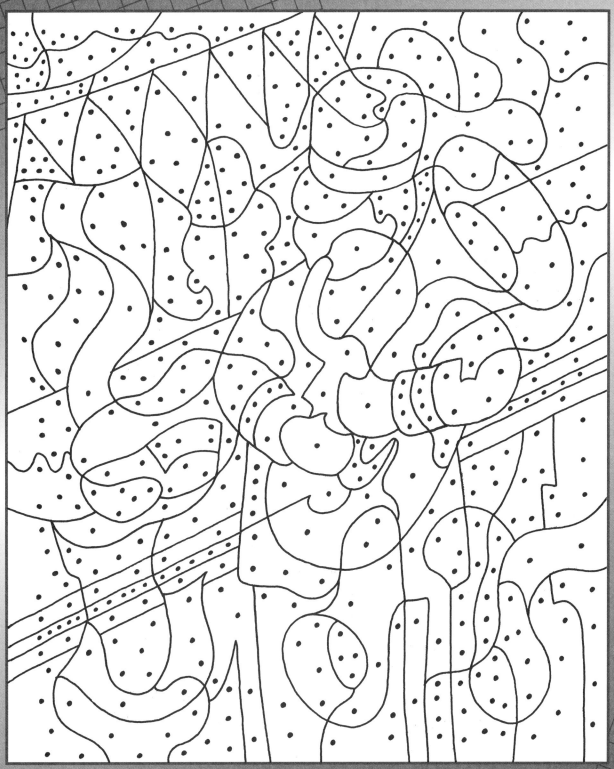

BIG TOP BUDGET

Each circus performer wants to do a few extra jobs around the big top to help pay for some things he or she bought. A person may do more than one job.

EXTRA JOBS AVAILABLE

1. HAND OUT PROGRAMS $ 9.75   _____
2. FIX TENT HOLES $ 17.00   _____
3. PAINT CIRCUS SIGN $ 12.00   _____
4. WASH FLAGS $ 10.00   _____
5. BLOW UP BALLOONS $ 5.75   _____
6. COLLECT TICKETS $ 5.25   _____
7. CLEAN CALLIOPE $ 15.00   _____
8. HANG BANNERS $ 16.00   _____

CURLY CLOWN
RUBBER NOSE $4.00
WHIRLY BOW TIE $3.25
FACE PAINT $10.00

SID STRONG
DUMBBELL $10.00
PENCIL $2.00
SKETCH PAD $3.50

But each job will only go to one person. Can you divide up the jobs so that everyone can earn enough extra money?

Hint on page 47

TARA TRAPEZE
HAIR CLIP $3.00
ROPE $8.00
SHOES $30.00

Answer on page 51

Illustration: Scott Peck

DANNY DOGBOY
FLEA COLLAR $7.00
HAT $8.00
DOG TREATS $2.00

MATHMAGIC

Here are two tricks in one.

Get a deck of cards. Shuffle them. Now have a guest pick any card.

Let her look at it and show it to others, but not to you.

Now have your guest put the card back into the deck.

Ask her to shuffle the deck a few times.

Now say a few magic words, then show the audience the top card of the deck.

Not only has the guest's card risen to the top of the pile, but you've magically changed it to a new card.

To find out how this trick works, turn to page 51.

Illustration: Marc Nadel

SAND ART

Answer on page 51

Can you draw this figure without going back over or crossing any lines?

Illustration: Barbara Gray

HINTS AND BRIGHT IDEAS

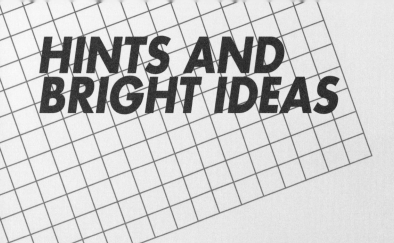

*T*hese hints may help with some of the trickier puzzles.

COVER

Compare some of the other bugs. We know 2 flies equal 1 snail. So that means 4 flies equal 3 caterpillars. How many ants equal 4 flies?

LINE UP (page 3)

Negative numbers go to the left of the 0. Negative numbers count back from -1, -2, -3, etc.

RECORD RESULTS (pages 4-5)

Remember when measuring distance, the longest distance wins. When measuring for time, the shortest period of time wins.

TAKING TEMPERATURES (page 7)

To find the average high, add together the seven high-temperature numbers. Then divide by 7.

WEIGHTING ROOM (pages 8-9)

Find the weight of each owner with his or her pet. Then find his or her weight without the pet. Subtract the smaller number from the larger number to find the pet's weight.

UPS AND DOWNS (page 14)

Start with the top floor and the bottom floor, then fill in the others.

100 DUCKS (page 15)

One of the ducks is 66.

KEEP MUM (pages 16-17)

A roll of wrapping covers 18 inches. Divide the heights by 18 to find the number of rolls.

WORDS WORTH (page 23)

The bottom lines of the staves are for the E. F is the space right above that. The scale only goes to G and then starts over alphabetically with the A note.

CAN CAN (page 30)
Odd numbers are 1, 3, 5, 7, and 9.

CIRCLE SURPRISE (page 31)
Remember that your lines must be straight. The top section has a 3, a 6, and a 9 in it. The bottom section has a 3, a 7, and an 8.

SUPER SHOPPER (pages 32-33)
To find the percentage off of a price, you may need to convert the percentage to a fraction. For instance, 25% is $\frac{1}{4}$ of the total. For the cleanser, divide $1.33 by 4. That's a total of $.33 off.

MATH PATH (pages 34-35)
There are no 9s given, only 6s.

DECIMAL DILEMMA (page 36)
Each decimal value stands for a percentage. Now think about how much space each fraction would fill up in a circle. $\frac{1}{2}$ is half the circle. Half of anything is 50%. So $\frac{1}{2}$ is equivalent to .50.

CROSS OUTS (page 37)
When you cross out a number, cross out the entire box, including the letter. We consider 0 to be an even number.

TAPE TIMES (pages 38-39)
Subtract the running time of the videotape from the time it has to be ready. This will give you the time to start.

LIBRARY LAUGHS (page 40)
Remember to consult the books to find the letter that matches each number.

BIG TOP BUDGET (pages 42-43)
One way to start would be to add up the amount of money each person needs. Then look for jobs that pay that amount.

ANSWERS

PLUG INS (page 6)

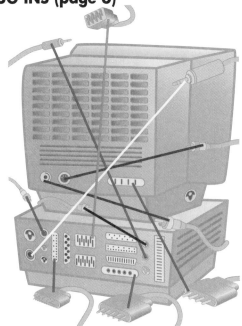

COVER
Eight ants

LINE UP (page 3)
```
-4  -3  -1  0  1  2  4  7
 A   S   E  A -L  I  N  E
```

Which animal can balance a ball, swim, and lie perfectly flat?
A SEA-LINE (a sea lion)

RECORD RESULTS (pages 4-5)
Softball Throw
  1st: Tawanna—16 feet
  2nd: Raul—14 feet
  3rd: Fekisha—10 feet
  4th: Michael—8 feet

5K Cycle Race
  1st: Barclay—8 minutes
  2nd: Ian—9 minutes
  3rd: Megan—10 minutes
  4th: Carlos—11 minutes

Basketball Shots for Accuracy
  1st: Farouk—46
  2nd: Ying—45
  3rd: Alexis—44
  4th: Ariana—43

Long Jump
  1st: Jasmine—30 inches
  2nd: Randy—28 inches
  3rd: Jason—27 inches
  4th: Dave—23 inches

Swimming (400-Meter Individual Medley)
  1st: Ruth—12 minutes
  2nd: Helen—14 minutes
  3rd: Elaine—15 minutes
  4th: George—19 minutes

TAKING TEMPERATURES (page 7)
1. Wednesday
2. Monday
3. 65.7°
4. 58°

WEIGHTING ROOM (pages 8-9)
Philip—84 pounds; Goldie—31 pounds
Daniel—97 pounds; Copperhead—17 pounds
Chris—142 pounds; Ironside—34 pounds
Joan—123 pounds; Tiny—8 pounds
Prudence—106 pounds; Silver—22 pounds
Ruby—139 pounds; Polo—6 pounds

STACKING STANLEY (page 10)
55 boxes

DOTS A LOT (page 11)

PLAY THE DOZENS (pages 12-13)

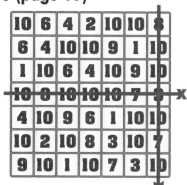

Crossword grid:

1 Across: HOURS
4 Across: DOZEN
5 Across: TIMES
6 Across: THIRTEEN
10 Across: ZEROS
11 Across: TWELVE
12 Across: SIDES

2 Down: ROMANS
3 Down: MONTHS
7 Down: INCH
8 Down: FEET
9 Down: GROSS
1 Down: H

UPS AND DOWNS (page 14)

10—Myra	5—Ellie
9—Christina	4—Ben
8—Jason	3—Craig
7—Stephanie	2—Darren
6—Jen	1—Tyler

100 DUCKS (page 15)

Here is our answer: 16 + 18 + 66 = 100

KEEP MUM (pages 16-17)

Mimi— 4 rolls (72 ÷ 18 = 4)
Mamie—3.5 rolls (63 ÷ 18 = 3.5)
Minnie—5 rolls (90 ÷ 18 = 5)
Fred—4.5 rolls (81 ÷ 18 = 4.5)
Max—3 rolls (54 ÷ 18 = 3)
A total of 20 rolls were used.

SIMONE SAYS (page 18)

A. 22 faces	D. 22 faces
B. 18 faces	E. 14 faces
C. 10 faces	F. 24 faces

FIND 50 (page 19)

GET COORDINATED (pages 20-21)

Why doesn't the piano work?
IT ONLY KNOWS HOW TO PLAY.

ODDS OR EVENS (page 22)

1. Even (60). An odd number plus an odd number will always equal an even number.
2. Odd (57). An odd number plus an even number will always equal an odd number.
3. Even (54). An even number plus an even number will always equal an even number.
4. Odd (221). An odd number times an odd number will always equal an odd number.
5. Even (640). An even number times an even number will always equal an even number.
6. Even (456). An odd number times an even number will always equal an even number.
7. Even (14). An odd number minus an odd number will always equal an even number.
8. Odd (27). An even number minus an odd number will always equal an odd number.
9. Even (2). An even number minus an even number will always equal an even number.
10. Odd (13). An odd number divided by an odd number will always equal an odd number.

WORDS WORTH (page 23)

SCRAMBLED PICTURE (pages 24-25)

WHAT'S THE PATTERN? (page 26)

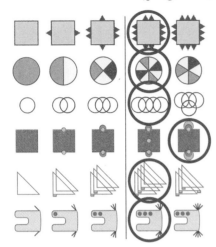

DON'T PEEK (page 27)
1. 13—one for each of the original colonies
2. Twice
3. 16—eight for each side
4. 64—eight rows of eight spaces
5. 5—1, 10, 11, 12
6. 1. The center box has four sides.
7. 8. A stop sign is an octagon.
8. 2—Alaska and Hawaii
9. None
10. 11. Did you forget the introduction question?

UPWARD BOUND (pages 28-29)

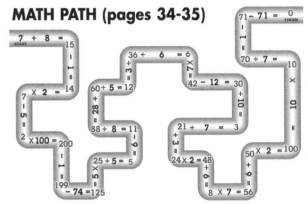

CAN CAN (page 30)
62935

CIRCLE SURPRISE (page 31)

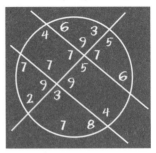

SUPER SHOPPER (pages 32-33)
Ginger Snaps—50% off 1 box
Cleano Cleanser—25% off
Perfect Pears—50¢ off 1 can
Crunch-A-Bunch Cereal—Half off 1 box
Zippy-Do Ketchup—50¢ off 1
Wipe 'Ems—50¢ off

MATH PATH (pages 34-35)

What do PLUMBERS eat for BREAKFAST?
WRENCH TOAST!

DECIMAL DILEMMA (page 36)
$\frac{1}{2}$ =.50; $\frac{1}{4}$ =.25; $\frac{1}{3}$ =.33; $\frac{3}{4}$ =.75; $\frac{2}{3}$ =.67

CROSS OUTS (page 37)

What has four legs and says, "Oom, oom?"
A COW WALKING BACKWARD